Spelling for Literacy
FOR AGES 7-8

Andrew Brodie

This second edition published 2015 by
Bloomsbury Publishing Plc

50 Bedford Square
London
WC1B 3DP
UK

1385 Broadway
New York
NY 10018
USA

www.bloomsbury.com

Bloomsbury is a registered trademark of Bloomsbury Publishing Plc

First published 2001 by Andrew Brodie Publications

Text © Andrew Brodie, 2015
Illustrations © Gaynor Berry, GCI Illustration, 2015
Design © Marcus Duck, 2015

British Library Cataloguing-in-Publication Data
A catalogue record for this book is available from the British Library.

ISBN 978-1-4729-1659-4

Library of Congress Cataloging-in-Publication Data
A catalog record for this book is available from the Library of Congress.

1 3 5 7 9 10 8 6 4 2

Printed and bound in India by Replika Press Pvt. Ltd.

This book is produced using paper that is made from wood grown in managed, sustainable forests.
It is natural, renewable and recyclable. The logging and manufacturing processes conform to the
environmental regulations of the country of origin.

To view more of our titles please visit www.bloomsbury.com

B L O O M S B U R Y

Contents

Introduction

The *Spelling for Literacy* series is well established as the leading spelling resource in use in schools across the United Kingdom. Now fully updated to meet the demands of the new National Curriculum, teachers can feel confident that each book covers all the spellings required for their year group.

This is the third book in the series, covering spellings suitable for Year 3 arising from the sounds, suffixes and prefixes that are specified as statutory requirements for Years 3 and 4. All the non-statutory example words listed in the National Curriculum are also included, together with other words that follow similar patterns.

As stated in the National Curriculum, Year 3 and Year 4 pupils should be reminded of the rules for adding suffixes that they have met in Key Stage 1. In this book they learn the use of more suffixes as well as a range of prefixes. They also learn about homophones and near homophones.

In a working environment of praise and enjoyment, the activities contained in this book will provide ample opportunities for meeting the statutory requirements as shown below.

Work for Year 3 and 4

STATUTORY REQUIREMENTS

- Adding suffixes beginning with vowel letters to words of more than one syllable
- The /ɪ/ sound spelt y elsewhere than at the end of words
- The /ʌ/ sound spelt ou
- More prefixes
- The suffix –ation
- The suffix –ly
- Words with endings sounding like /ʒə/ or /tʃə/
- Endings which sound like /ʒən/
- The suffix –ous
- Endings which sound like /ʃən/, spelt –tion, –sion, –ssion, –cian

- Words with the /k/ sound spelt ch (Greek in origin)
- Words with the /ʃ/ sound spelt ch (mostly French in origin)
- Words ending with the /g/ sound spelt – gue and the /k/ sound spelt –que (French in origin)
- Words with the /s/ sound spelt sc (Latin in origin)
- Words with the /eɪ/ sound spelt ei, eigh, or ey
- Possessive apostrophe with plural words
- Homophones and near-homophones

Suggestions for using this book...

The words are arranged in sets, usually of ten words but in some cases twelve or sixteen. Each set of words is used in three styles of sheet:

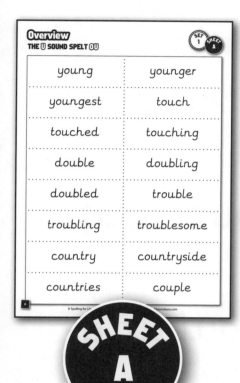

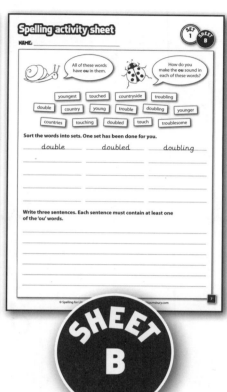

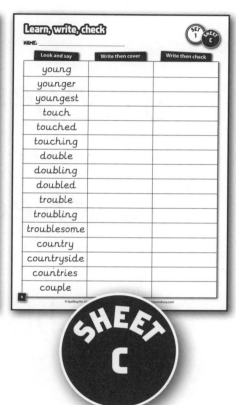

Overview

- Can be displayed on-screen for discussion.

- Can be printed out and displayed as 'Words of the Week'.

Spelling activity sheet

- To be used as part of a lesson.

- A perfect follow-up activity for the learning that has taken place using Sheet A and ideal for homework.

Learn, write, check

- Children look at the words, say them out loud and write them down, before covering the first two columns, re-writing the words and then checking them.

- Can be used in class.

- Can be used as homework.

young	younger
youngest	touch
touched	touching
double	doubling
doubled	trouble
troubling	troublesome
country	countryside
countries	couple

Spelling activity sheet

NAME: _____

All of these words have **ou** in them.

How do you make the **ou** sound in each of these words?

| youngest | touched | countryside | troubling |

| double | country | young | trouble | doubling | younger |

| countries | touching | doubled | touch | troublesome |

Sort the words into sets. One set has been done for you.

double	*doubled*	*doubling*
_____	_____	_____
_____	_____	_____
_____	_____	_____
_____	_____	_____

Write three sentences. Each sentence must contain at least one of the 'ou' words.

_____

_____

_____

_____

_____

Learn, write, check

NAME: _____

Look and say	Write then cover	Write then check
young		
younger		
youngest		
touch		
touched		
touching		
double		
doubling		
doubled		
trouble		
troubling		
troublesome		
country		
countryside		
countries		
couple		

sing	singing
ring	ringing
walk	walking
jump	jumping
paint	painting
dress	dressing
rest	resting
call	calling

Spelling activity sheet

NAME: _____

These words have two consonants at the end.

We don't change them when adding **ing**.

Add 'ing' to the words on the left. The first one has been done for you.

sing ⟶ singing

ring ⟶ _____

walk ⟶ _____

jump ⟶ _____

paint ⟶ _____

dress ⟶ _____

rest ⟶ _____

call ⟶ _____

Fill in the missing words using some of the 'ing' words that you have made.

When I am _____ I put on my socks first.

When we went for a walk, Gina kept _____ up to touch the leaves.

I could hear Tom _____ my name.

I was _____ a picture.

The bells were _____ and I was _____ a song.

Now make up some sentences of your own, using words from the list above.

Learn, write, check

NAME: _____

Look and say	Write then cover	Write then check
sing		
singing		
ring		
ringing		
walk		
walking		
jump		
jumping		
paint		
painting		
dress		
dressing		
rest		
resting		
call		
calling		

sleep	sleeping
dream	dreaming
feel	feeling
shout	shouting
sail	sailing
boil	boiling
peel	peeling
speak	speaking

Spelling activity sheet

NAME: _____

These words have two vowels before the final consonant.

We don't change them when we add **ing**.

Add 'ing' to the words on the left. The first one has been done for you.

sleep	→	sleeping
dream	→	_____
feel	→	_____
shout	→	_____
sail	→	_____
boil	→	_____
peel	→	_____
speak	→	_____

Fill in the missing words. The first one has been done for you.
Try to find a third pair of words for each set that use the same two vowels.

sleep	sail	eat	look
↓	↓	↓	↓
sleeping	_____	_____	_____
sweep	nail	treat	cook
↓	↓	↓	↓
_____	_____	_____	_____
↓	↓	↓	↓
_____	_____	_____	_____

Learn, write, check

NAME: _____

Look and say	Write then cover	Write then check
sleep		
sleeping		
dream		
dreaming		
feel		
feeling		
shout		
shouting		
sail		
sailing		
boil		
boiling		
peel		
peeling		
speak		
speaking		

run	running
hop	hopping
sit	sitting
skip	skipping
step	stepping
grip	gripping
shut	shutting
win	winning

Spelling activity sheet

NAME: _____

Each of these words ends with a consonant with one vowel in front of it.

If we want to add **ing** we must double the consonant.

Add 'ing' to the words on the left. The first one has been done for you.

run ⟶ running

hop ⟶ _____

sit ⟶ _____

skip ⟶ _____

step ⟶ _____

grip ⟶ _____

shut ⟶ _____

win ⟶ _____

Fill in the missing words using some of the 'ing' words that you have made.

Jasdeep is _____ with her rope.

The builder is _____ the hammer very tightly.

We must go because the shop is _____.

Here are some more words, which follow the same spelling pattern:

hum   win   spin   swim   stop

In your book, add 'ing' to each word – don't forget to double the consonant. Write a sentence for each new word that you have made.

© Spelling for Literacy for ages 7-8 • Andrew Brodie 2015 • www.bloomsbury.com

Learn, write, check

NAME: _____

Look and say	Write then cover	Write then check
run		
running		
hop		
hopping		
sit		
sitting		
skip		
skipping		
step		
stepping		
grip		
gripping		
shut		
shutting		
win		
winning		

hope	hoping
come	coming
smile	smiling
take	taking
care	caring
make	making
divide	dividing
stare	staring

Spelling activity sheet

NAME: _____

These words have a vowel, then a consonant, and end with letter **e**.

If we want to add **ing** we must take off the letter **e**.

Add 'ing' to the words on the left. The first one has been done for you.

hope → hoping

come → _____

smile → _____

take → _____

care → _____

make → _____

divide → _____

stare → _____

Find the root words for these words, which end with ing.
The first one has been done for you.

phoning → phone

shining → _____

tuning → _____

rhyming → _____

timing → _____

Choose five of the 'ing' words from this page. Write a sentence for each one.

19

Learn, write, check

NAME: _____

Look and say	Write then cover	Write then check
hope		
hoping		
come		
coming		
smile		
smiling		
take		
taking		
care		
caring		
make		
making		
divide		
dividing		
stare		
staring		

pan	pancake
week	weekend
goal	goalkeeper
break	breakfast
stairs	upstairs
downstairs	any
anybody	anyone
anything	anywhere

Spelling activity sheet

NAME: _____

How many words can you think of that end with **body**?

I can think of **anybody**, **nobody**, **somebody** and **everybody**.

Make some compound words using the start words and end words below. Some of them can be used more than once.

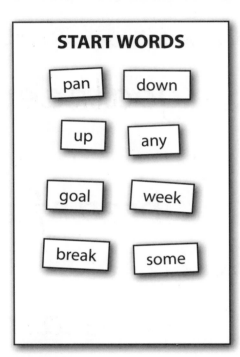

START WORDS

pan down

up any

goal week

break some

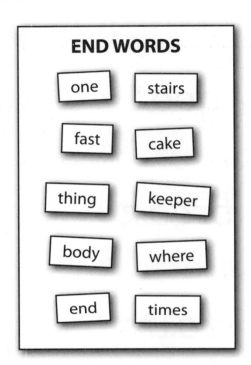

END WORDS

one stairs

fast cake

thing keeper

body where

end times

START WORD		END WORD		COMPOUND WORD
_____	→	_____	→	_____
_____	→	_____	→	_____
_____	→	_____	→	_____
_____	→	_____	→	_____
_____	→	_____	→	_____
_____	→	_____	→	_____
_____	→	_____	→	_____
_____	→	_____	→	_____

© Spelling for Literacy for ages 7-8 • Andrew Brodie 2015 • www.bloomsbury.com

Learn, write, check

NAME: _____

SET 6 · SHEET C

Look and say	Write then cover	Write then check
pan		
pancake		
week		
weekend		
goal		
goalkeeper		
break		
breakfast		
stairs		
upstairs		
downstairs		
any		
anybody		
anyone		
anything		
anywhere		

eleven	twelve
thirteen	fourteen
fifteen	sixteen
seventeen	eighteen
nineteen	twenty
thirty	forty
fifty	sixty
seventy	eighty

Spelling activity sheet

NAME: _____

Sometimes we write numbers using numerals…

… and sometimes we use words.

Write the correct words to match the numbers written in numerals.

20 _____   13 _____

17 _____   80 _____

11 _____   12 _____

60 _____   70 _____

16 _____   14 _____

19 _____   40 _____

50 _____   18 _____

30 _____   15 _____

Copy the words below. Remember, these words have a letter u:

four   _____

fourteen   _____

But this word does not:

forty   _____

NAME: _____

Look and say	Write then cover	Write then check
eleven		
twelve		
thirteen		
fourteen		
fifteen		
sixteen		
seventeen		
eighteen		
nineteen		
twenty		
thirty		
forty		

ninety	hundred
thousand	million
metre	centimetre
millimetre	kilometre
gram	kilogram
litre	millilitre
second	minute
hour	month

Spelling activity sheet

NAME: _____

 On this page we have some big numbers…

 … and some words to do with measuring.

**Draw arrows to match each numeral to the correct number word.
Then copy the words.**

1000

1000000

90

100

_____ninety_____ _____

_____hundred_____ _____

_____thousand_____ _____

_____million_____ _____

Label the hands on the clock, using these words: | minute | hour | second |

_____ hand

_____ hand

_____ hand

Write the correct measurement word for each abbreviation.

MEASUREMENT WORDS

| metre | centimetre |

| millimetre | kilometre |

| gram | kilogram |

| litre | millilitre |

cm _____

km _____

m _____

l _____

ml _____

kg _____

mm _____

g _____

Learn, write, check

NAME: _____

Look and say	Write then cover	Write then check
ninety		
hundred		
thousand		
million		
metre		
centimetre		
millimetre		
kilometre		
gram		
kilogram		
litre		
millilitre		
second		
minute		
hour		
month		

happy	unhappy
tidy	untidy
lucky	unlucky
usual	unusual
zip	unzip
tie	untie
fair	unfair
kind	unkind

Spelling activity sheet

NAME: _____

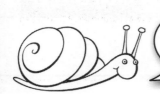 We can make the opposites of some words…

 … just by putting **un** at the start.

Add 'un' to the words on the left. The first one has been done for you.

happy	⟶	unhappy
tidy	⟶	_____
lucky	⟶	_____
usual	⟶	_____
zip	⟶	_____
tie	⟶	_____
fair	⟶	_____
kind	⟶	_____

Fill in the gaps using the words in the right hand column.

I was very _____ when I got told off.

I had to _____ my coat because I was so hot.

The hoops were tied together so I had to _____ them.

You should not be _____ to other people.

Try to find three other words that can have 'un' added at the start.
Write your pairs of words here.

_____   _____

_____   _____

_____   _____

Learn, write, check

NAME: _____

Look and say	Write then cover	Write then check
happy		
unhappy		
tidy		
untidy		
lucky		
unlucky		
usual		
unusual		
zip		
unzip		
tie		
untie		
fair		
unfair		
kind		
unkind		

forget	forgetting
forgotten	begin
beginning	beginner
prefer	preferred
preferring	garden
gardening	gardened
gardener	limit
limited	limitation

Spelling activity sheet

NAME: _____

Try saying these words out loud. When the last syllable of a word is stressed…

… we usually have to double the consonant before adding an ending.

Add 'ing' to the words on the left. The first one has been done for you.

forget ⟶ forgetting

begin ⟶ _____

prefer ⟶ _____

When the last syllable of a word is not stressed…

…we don't have to double the consonant before adding an ending.

Add 'ing' to the words on the left. The first one has been done for you.

garden ⟶ gardening

limit ⟶ _____

| forgotten | beginner | preferred | gardener | limited |

Fill in the missing words.

The _____ planted some roses by the path because he said he _____ to have them close to where we walk. He had _____ that I was just a _____ so he didn't know that my gardening skills were _____ to mowing the lawn!

34

Learn, write, check

NAME: _____

Look and say	Write then cover	Write then check
forget		
forgetting		
forgotten		
begin		
beginning		
beginner		
prefer		
preferred		
preferring		
garden		
gardening		
gardened		
gardener		
limit		
limited		
limitation		

appoint	disappoint
agree	disagree
obey	disobey
connect	disconnect
appear	disappear
behave	misbehave
lead	mislead
spell	misspell

© Spelling for Literacy for ages 7-8 • Andrew Brodie 2015 • www.bloomsbury.com

Spelling activity sheet

NAME: _____

We can change the meaning of some words …

… by adding the prefix **dis** or the prefix **mis**.

Add 'dis' or 'mis' to the words on the left. The first one has been done for you.

agree → disagree

spell → _____

connect → _____

appoint → _____

lead → _____

appear → _____

obey → _____

behave → _____

Now try these.

loyal → _____

print → _____

obedient → _____

match → _____

Write three sentences. Each sentence must contain a word beginning with 'dis' or 'mis'.

_____

_____

_____

_____

_____

_____

Learn, write, check

NAME: _____

Look and say	Write then cover	Write then check
appoint		
disappoint		
agree		
disagree		
obey		
disobey		
connect		
disconnect		
appear		
disappear		
behave		
misbehave		
lead		
mislead		
spell		
misspell		

38

comb	bomb
thumb	crumb
lamb	numb
climb	calf
calves	half
halves	calm
palm	could
should	would

Spelling activity sheet

NAME: _____

On this page, seven words have silent **b**…

… and nine words have silent **l**.

| halves | could | crumb | palm | should | bomb | half | climb |

| calm | calf | comb | thumb | calves | would | lamb | numb |

Sort the words into two sets.

Silent **b** words	Silent **l** words
_____	_____
_____	_____
_____	_____
_____	_____
_____	_____
_____	_____
_____	_____
	_____
	_____

Write a sentence that includes the words 'lamb' and 'calf'.

_____

_____

Now try writing a sentence that includes five words with silent letters. This could be tricky!

_____

_____

_____

40

Learn, write, check

NAME: _____

Look and say	Write then cover	Write then check
comb		
bomb		
thumb		
crumb		
lamb		
numb		
climb		
calf		
calves		
half		
halves		
calm		
palm		
could		
should		
would		

knee	kneel
knife	knives
know	knock
gnat	gnome
grow	write
wrist	wrap
when	where
honest	rhyme

Spelling activity sheet

NAME: _____

On this page, some words have silent **k**, some have silent **g**, some have silent **w**…

… and some words have silent **h**.

gnome	rhyme	wrap	gnat	gnaw	where

knock	knee	wrist	know	write	honest

Sort the words into sets.

Silent **k** words	Silent **w** words	Silent **h** words	Silent **g** words
_____	_____	_____	_____
_____	_____	_____	_____
_____	_____	_____	_____

Write a sentence that includes the words 'know' and 'honest'.

_____

_____

Now try writing a sentence that includes five words with silent letters. This could be tricky!

_____

_____

_____

_____

Learn, write, check

NAME: _____

Look and say	Write then cover	Write then check
knee		
kneel		
knife		
knives		
know		
knock		
gnat		
gnome		
gnaw		
write		
wrist		
wrap		
when		
where		
honest		
rhyme		

© Spelling for Literacy for ages 7-8 • Andrew Brodie 2015 • www.bloomsbury.com

build	rebuild
visit	revisit
play	replay
write	rewrite
cycle	recycle
place	replace
turn	return
fresh	refresh

Spelling activity sheet

NAME: _____

 The prefix **re**…

 … usually means **to do something again**.

Add 're' to the words on the left. The first one has been done for you.

build   ⟶   rebuild

visit   ⟶   _____

play   ⟶   _____

write   ⟶   _____

cycle   ⟶   _____

place   ⟶   _____

turn   ⟶   _____

Copy these two words that start with 'pre'.

prepare _____

prefix _____

Can you think of any other words that start with 'pre'?
Use a dictionary to help you find them.

_____ _____ _____

_____ _____ _____

Learn, write, check

NAME: _____

Look and say	Write then cover	Write then check
build		
rebuild		
visit		
revisit		
play		
replay		
write		
rewrite		
cycle		
recycle		
place		
replace		
turn		
return		
fresh		
refresh		

cycle	bicycle
recycle	tricycle
appear	disappear
visible	invisible
normal	abnormal
view	preview
review	interview
marine	submarine

48

Spelling activity sheet

NAME: _____

Some words can have several different prefixes added to them.

How many prefixes can be added to the word **cycle**?

cycle ⟶ ___+ bi___ ⟶ bicycle

cycle ⟶ ___+ re___ ⟶ recycle

cycle ⟶ ___+ tri___ ⟶ tricycle

Make new words by adding the prefixes shown to the root words.

cycle ___+ bi___ ⟶ _____

cycle ___+ re___ ⟶ _____

cycle ___+ tri___ ⟶ _____

appear ___+ dis___ ⟶ _____

visible ___+ in___ ⟶ _____

normal ___+ ab___ ⟶ _____

view ___+ pre___ ⟶ _____

view ___+ re___ ⟶ _____

view ___+ inter___ ⟶ _____

marine ___+ sub___ ⟶ _____

Can you think of any other words that start with the prefix 'inter'?

_____   _____   _____

Learn, write, check

NAME: _____

Look and say	Write then cover	Write then check
cycle		
bicycle		
recycle		
tricycle		
appear		
disappear		
visible		
invisible		
normal		
abnormal		
view		
preview		
review		
interview		
marine		
submarine		

Overview
PREFIXES

behave	misbehave
sense	nonsense
fiction	non-fiction
stop	non-stop
import	export
interior	exterior
star	co-star
clockwise	anti-clockwise

© Spelling for Literacy for ages 7-8 • Andrew Brodie 2015 • www.bloomsbury.com

Spelling activity sheet

NAME: _____

Remember: prefixes are extra parts added to the start of some words.

They change the meaning of the words.

Practise writing the word pairs. To make it harder, try covering the words on the left.

behave	_____	import	_____
misbehave	_____	export	_____
sense	_____	interior	_____
nonsense	_____	exterior	_____
fiction	_____	star	_____
non-fiction	_____	co-star	_____
stop	_____	clockwise	_____
non-stop	_____	anticlockwise	_____

Some of the words above give the answers to this crossword.

CLUES DOWN
2. Not making sense
7. Outside a building
8. Don't go

CLUES ACROSS
1. The direction of a clock's hands
3. When you are good, you _____
4. The inside of a building
5. Story books about people or events that are not real
6. A famous person or something that twinkles in the night sky

52

Learn, write, check

NAME: _____

Look and say	Write then cover	Write then check
behave		
misbehave		
sense		
nonsense		
fiction		
non-fiction		
stop		
non-stop		
import		
export		
interior		
exterior		
star		
co-star		
clockwise		
anti-clockwise		

mature	immature
mortal	immortal
possible	impossible
patient	impatient
perfect	imperfect
market	supermarket
man	superman
star	superstar

Spelling activity sheet

NAME: _____

 Some words can have the prefix **im**, which usually means **not** or **the opposite of**.

 Some words can have the prefix **super**, which usually means **more**.

Choose the prefix 'im' or the prefix 'super' to add to the words on the left to make new words.

WORD	PREFIX		NEW WORD
market	_____	⟶	_____
star	_____	⟶	_____
mature	_____	⟶	_____
man	_____	⟶	_____
mortal	_____	⟶	_____
possible	_____	⟶	_____
perfect	_____	⟶	_____
patient	_____	⟶	_____

Write a sentence that includes the word 'impossible'.

_____

_____

Write a sentence that includes a word with the prefix 'super'.

_____

_____

Learn, write, check

NAME: _____

Look and say	Write then cover	Write then check
mature		
immature		
mortal		
immortal		
possible		
impossible		
patient		
impatient		
perfect		
imperfect		
market		
supermarket		
man		
superman		
star		
superstar		

do	redo
new	renew
wind	rewind
turn	return
appear	reappear
decorate	redecorate
divide	subdivide
marine	submarine

© Spelling for Literacy for ages 7-8 • Andrew Brodie 2015 • www.bloomsbury.com

Spelling activity sheet

NAME: _____

Some words can have the prefix **re**, which usually means **again**.

Some words can have the prefix **sub**, which usually means **under** or **below**.

Choose the prefix 're' or the prefix 'sub' to add to the words on the left to make new words.

WORD	PREFIX		NEW WORD
new	_____	→	_____
appear	_____	→	_____
marine	_____	→	_____
do	_____	→	_____
wind	_____	→	_____
decorate	_____	→	_____
divide	_____	→	_____
turn	_____	→	_____

Write a sentence that includes the word 'disappear'.

_____

_____

Write a sentence that includes a word with the prefix 'sub'.

_____

_____

Learn, write, check

NAME: _____

Look and say	Write then cover	Write then check
do		
redo		
new		
renew		
wind		
rewind		
turn		
return		
appear		
reappear		
decorate		
redecorate		
divide		
subdivide		
marine		
submarine		

inform	informing
informed	information
adore	adoration
sense	sensation
prepare	preparing
prepared	preparation
admire	admired
admiring	admiration

Spelling activity sheet

NAME: _____

All of these words can be sorted into sets.

How quickly can you sort them and still keep your work tidy?

| information | admired | preparing | sensation | adore | preparation |

| admire | informing | admiration | adoration | informed | sense |

| inform | prepared | admiring | prepare |

Sort the words into sets. One set has been done for you.

admire _____ _____ _____ _____

admired _____ _____ _____ _____

admiring _____ _____ _____ _____

admiration _____ _____ _____ _____

Write five sentences. Each sentence must contain at least one of the words from each set.

_____

_____

_____

_____

_____

_____

_____

_____

Learn, write, check

NAME: _____

Look and say	Write then cover	Write then check
inform		
informing		
informed		
information		
adore		
adoration		
sense		
sensation		
prepare		
preparing		
prepared		
preparation		
admire		
admired		
admiring		
admiration		

Overview
SUFFIXES

sad	sadly
complete	completely
actual	actually
usual	usually
final	finally
comic	comical
comically	accident
accidental	accidentally

Spelling activity sheet

NAME: _____

Some words can have two suffixes added to them. A suffix goes at the end of a word.

For example, **accident** can have **al** then **ly** added to it.

accident ⟶ _____ + al ⟶ _____ + ly

↓   ↓

accidental   accidentally

Make new words by adding the prefixes shown to the root words.

accident	+ al	⟶	_____
comic	+ al	⟶	_____
sad	+ ly	⟶	_____
complete	+ ly	⟶	_____
actual	+ ly	⟶	_____
final	+ ly	⟶	_____
accidental	+ ly	⟶	_____
comical	+ ly	⟶	_____
usual	+ ly	⟶	_____

Can you make two other words using the word 'magic'?

_____   _____

Write two sentences, each one containing at least one of the words above.

_____

_____

_____

_____

Learn, write, check

NAME: _____

Look and say	Write then cover	Write then check
sad		
sadly		
complete		
completely		
actual		
actually		
usual		
usually		
final		
finally		
comic		
comical		
comically		
accident		
accidental		
accidentally		

happy	happily
happiness	anger
angry	angrily
tidy	tidily
untidy	gentle
gently	gentleness
simple	simply
simpler	simplest

Spelling activity sheet

NAME: _____

When we add suffixes to the word **happy**…

… we have to change the **y** to an **i**.

| happiness | simplest | gentle | angry | simpler | happy |

| anger | gentleness | simple | untidy | angrily | happily |

| tidy | gently | tidily | simply |

Sort the words into sets. One set has been done for you.

tidy				
untidy				
tidily				

Write five sentences. Each sentence must contain at least one of the words from each set.

_____

_____

_____

_____

_____

_____

_____

_____

_____

Learn, write, check

NAME: _____

Look and say	Write then cover	Write then check
happy		
happily		
happiness		
anger		
angry		
angrily		
tidy		
tidily		
untidy		
gentle		
gently		
gentleness		
simple		
simply		
simpler		
simplest		

68

© Spelling for Literacy for ages 7-8 • Andrew Brodie 2015 • www.bloomsbury.com

measure	measured
measuring	treasure
treasured	treasuring
please	pleased
pleasing	pleasure
enclose	enclosing
enclosed	enclosure
leisure	leisurely

Spelling activity sheet

NAME: _____

All of these words can be sorted into sets.

How quickly can you sort them and still keep your work tidy?

measuring	leisurely	treasuring	treasure	pleased	enclosure
pleasure	measured	treasured	measure	enclosed	pleasing
	please	enclose	leisure	enclosing	

Sort the words into sets. One set has been done for you.

leisure _____ _____ _____ _____

leisurely _____ _____ _____ _____

_____ _____ _____ _____ _____

_____ _____ _____ _____ _____

Write five sentences. Each sentence must contain at least one of the words from each set.

_____

_____

_____

_____

_____

_____

_____

_____

_____

_____

Learn, write, check

SET 22 SHEET C

NAME: _____

Look and say	Write then cover	Write then check
measure		
measured		
measuring		
treasure		
treasured		
treasuring		
please		
pleased		
pleasing		
pleasure		
enclose		
enclosing		
enclosed		
enclosure		
leisure		
leisurely		

is not	isn't
was not	wasn't
did not	didn't
does not	doesn't
will not	won't
cannot	can't
could not	couldn't
should not	shouldn't

Spelling activity sheet

NAME: _____

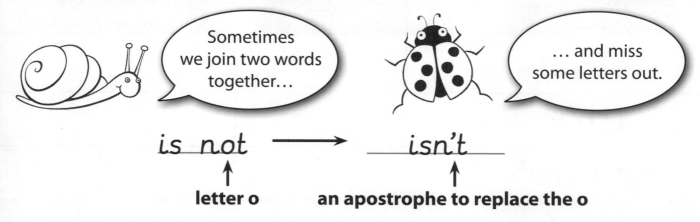

Sometimes we join two words together…

… and miss some letters out.

is not   →   isn't

↑ letter o   ↑ an apostrophe to replace the o

Join each set of words on the left to the correct word on the right. The first one has been done for you.

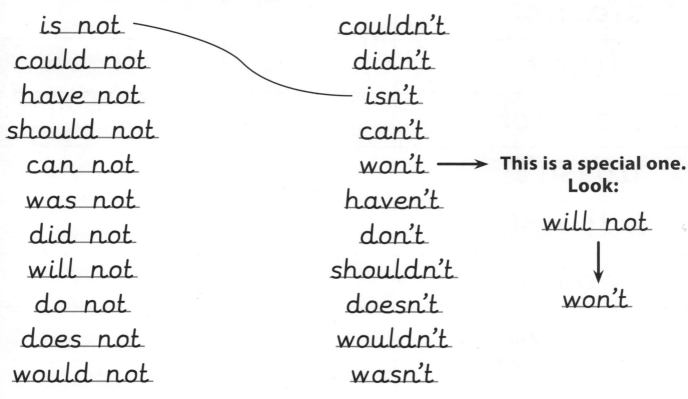

is not	couldn't
could not	didn't
have not	isn't
should not	can't
can not	won't
was not	haven't
did not	don't
will not	shouldn't
do not	doesn't
does not	wouldn't
would not	wasn't

won't → **This is a special one. Look:**

will not ↓ won't

Fill in a gap with a word that has been shortened using an apostrophe.

I _____ go to town because
there _____ enough room on the bus.
My brother _____ get up this morning.
I said to him, "If you _____ get up,
you _____ come swimming."

Learn, write, check

NAME: _____

Look and say	Write then cover	Write then check
is not		
isn't		
was not		
wasn't		
did not		
didn't		
does not		
doesn't		
will not		
won't		
cannot		
can't		
could not		
couldn't		
should not		
shouldn't		

teach	teacher
farm	farmer
drive	driver
mine	miner
babysit	babysitter
run	runner
shop	shopper
spin	spinner

Spelling activity sheet

NAME: _____

Sometimes we have to change the end of a word when we want to add **er**…

… but sometimes we don't have to change the end.

For these words we just add 'er':

teach ⟶ _____   farm ⟶ _____

For these words we take off e then add 'er':

mine ⟶ _____   drive ⟶ _____

For these words we double the end consonant, then add 'er':

babysit ⟶ _____   run ⟶ _____

shop ⟶ _____   spin ⟶ _____

Check that your words look exactly like these:

teacher   miner   babysitter   shopper

farmer   driver   runner   spinner

Find the correct word to match each clue:

Operates a car ⟶ _____

Looks after animals and grows food ⟶ _____

Works at school ⟶ _____

Looks after children when their mum and dad are out ⟶ _____

Runs in race ⟶ _____

Learn, write, check

NAME: _____

Look and say	Write then cover	Write then check
teach		
teacher		
farm		
farmer		
drive		
driver		
mine		
miner		
babysit		
babysitter		
run		
runner		
shop		
shopper		
spin		
spinner		

teach	teacher
catch	catcher
rich	richer
stretch	stretcher
creature	furniture
picture	nature
natural	naturally
adventure	adventurous

© Spelling for Literacy for ages 7-8 • Andrew Brodie 2015 • www.bloomsbury.com

Spelling activity sheet

NAME: _____

All of the words on this page have the sound **ch**…

… but it can be spelt in different ways.

| teach | catch | richer | stretch | catcher | teacher | rich |

| stretcher | furniture | creature | nature | picture | adventure |

Sort the words into sets.

The sound **ch** with the spelling **ch**	The sound **ch** with the spelling **tch**	The sound **ch** with the spelling **ture**
_____	_____	_____
_____	_____	_____
_____	_____	_____
_____	_____	_____
_____	_____	_____

Write three sentences. Each sentence must include one of these words:

| natural | furniture | adventurous |

_____

_____

_____

_____

_____

_____

Learn, write, check

SET 25 · SHEET C

NAME: _____

Look and say	Write then cover	Write then check
teach		
teacher		
catch		
catcher		
rich		
richer		
stretch		
stretcher		
creature		
furniture		
picture		
nature		
natural		
naturally		
adventure		
adventurous		

poison	poisoning
poisoned	poisonous
danger	dangerous
mountain	mountainous
fame	famous
vary	various
tremendous	enormous
jealous	jealousy

Spelling activity sheet

NAME: _____

Lots of these words…

… include the letters **ous**.

| poison | poisoning | poisoned | poisonous | danger | dangerous |

| mountain | mountainous | fame | famous | vary | various |

| tremendous | enormous | jealous | jealousy |

Add the suffix 'ous' to the root words.

poison ⟶ _____

danger ⟶ _____

mountain ⟶ _____

fame ⟶ _____

vary ⟶ _____

List the words from the word bank that you have not already used.

_____ _____ _____

_____ _____ _____

Write three sentences. Each sentence must include one of the words from the word bank.

_____

_____

_____

_____

_____

Learn, write, check

NAME: _____

Look and say	Write then cover	Write then check
poison		
poisoning		
poisoned		
poisonous		
danger		
dangerous		
mountain		
mountainous		
fame		
famous		
vary		
various		
tremendous		
enormous		
jealous		
jealousy		

invent	invention
inject	injection
act	action
hesitate	hesitation
complete	completion
describe	description
detect	detection
reflect	reflection

Spelling activity sheet

NAME: _____

Some words don't need to be changed much when we add the suffix **tion**…

… but some words do need to be changed, so watch out!

Add the suffix 'tion' to the root words.
Be careful, because some words need to be changed.

invent   ⟶ _____

hesitate   ⟶ _____

describe   ⟶ _____

reflect   ⟶ _____

inject   ⟶ _____

detect   ⟶ _____

complete   ⟶ _____

act   ⟶ _____

Write a short sentence for each of the 'tion' words.

_____

_____

_____

_____

_____

_____

_____

Learn, write, check

NAME: _____

Look and say	Write then cover	Write then check
invent		
invention		
inject		
injection		
act		
action		
hesitate		
hesitation		
complete		
completion		
describe		
description		
detect		
detection		
reflect		
reflection		

© Spelling for Literacy for ages 7-8 • Andrew Brodie 2015 • www.bloomsbury.com

express	expression
discuss	discussing
discussed	discussion
confess	confession
permit	permission
admit	admission
possess	possession
process	procession

Spelling activity sheet

NAME: _____

 Some words don't need to be changed much when using the suffix **ssion**…

 … but look out for those that do!

Add the suffix 'ssion' to the root words.
Be careful, because some words need to be changed.

express   ⟶   _____

permit   ⟶   _____

discuss   ⟶   _____

admit   ⟶   _____

confess   ⟶   _____

possess   ⟶   _____

process   ⟶   _____

Now add the suffixes 'ing' and 'ed' to the root words. Be careful, because some words need to be changed. One has been done for you.

permit ⟶ permitting ⟶ permitted

admit ⟶ _____ ⟶ _____

express ⟶ _____ ⟶ _____

discuss ⟶ _____ ⟶ _____

confess ⟶ _____ ⟶ _____

process ⟶ _____ ⟶ _____

possess ⟶ _____ ⟶ _____

Learn, write, check

NAME: _____

Look and say	Write then cover	Write then check
express		
expression		
discuss		
discussing		
discussed		
discussion		
confess		
confession		
permit		
permission		
admit		
admission		
possess		
possession		
process		
procession		

chef	chalet
machine	brochure
league	tongue
dialogue	analogue
plague	antique
unique	mosque
cheque	grotesque
grotesquely	uniquely

90

Spelling activity sheet

NAME: _____

This page has some unusual spellings.

How quickly can you sort the words into sets?

| chef | chalet | machine | brochure | league | tongue |

| dialogue | analogue | plague | antique | unique | mosque |

| cheque | grotesque | grotesquely | uniquely |

Sound **sh** spelt with **ch**	Sound **g** spelt with **gue**	Sound **k** spelt with **que**
_____	_____	_____
_____	_____	_____
_____	_____	_____
_____	_____	_____
_____	_____	_____
_____	_____	_____
_____	_____	_____

Fill in the missing words.

My mum booked the ski _____ and paid with a _____.

The _____ cooked a lovely meal.

My little sister poked her _____ out at me!

We bought an old clock in an _____ shop.

Learn, write, check

NAME: _____

Look and say	Write then cover	Write then check
chef		
chalet		
machine		
brochure		
league		
tongue		
dialogue		
analogue		
plague		
antique		
unique		
mosque		
cheque		
grotesque		
grotesquely		
uniquely		

© Spelling for Literacy for ages 7-8 • Andrew Brodie 2015 • www.bloomsbury.com

Overview
SOME SPELLINGS OF THE AE SOUND

vein	weigh
weight	eight
eighth	eighty
eighteen	neigh
neighbour	neighbourly
neighbourhood	high
they	obey
straight	sleigh

Spelling activity sheet

NAME: _____

This page has words with the sound **ay**…

… but none of them are spelt **ay**!

vein · weigh · high · eight · neigh · obey · eighteen

neighbour · eighth · weight · straight · neighbourhood

sleigh · they · neighbourly · eighty

Which of the words have the spelling 'eigh' for the sound 'ay'?

_____ _____ _____ _____

_____ _____ _____ _____

_____ _____ _____

Which of the words have the spelling 'ey' for the sound 'ay'?

_____ _____

Which of the words has the spelling 'aigh' for the sound 'ay'?

_____

Fill in the missing words.

My next door _____ is a good friend of mine.

The horse gave a _____ when I sat on
its back – I was very _____ up.

I need a ruler to draw a _____ line.

Write a sentence including the word 'eight'.

_____

_____

Learn, write, check

NAME: _____

Look and say	Write then cover	Write then check
vein		
weigh		
weight		
eight		
eighth		
eighty		
eighteen		
sleigh		
neigh		
neighbour		
neighbourly		
neighbourhood		
high		
they		
obey		
straight		

accept	except
affect	effect
ball	bawl
berry	bury
brake	break
fair	fare
grate	great
groan	grown

Spelling activity sheet

NAME: _____

Some words sound the same or nearly the same…

… but they are spelt differently.

Match the words on the left to the words on the right.
The first one has been done for you.

ball   fare

grown   berry

except   bawl

break   groan

bury   great

grate   brake

fair   accept

affect   effect

Choose the correct word to fill each gap.

The baby began to _____ loudly.

My gran said I had _____ a lot.

The squirrel decided to _____ some nuts in my back garden.

I had to have the correct _____ when I got on the bus.

Learn, write, check

NAME: _____

Look and say	Write then cover	Write then check
accept		
except		
affect		
effect		
ball		
bawl		
berry		
bury		
brake		
break		
fair		
fare		
grate		
great		
groan		
grown		

© Spelling for Literacy for ages 7-8 • Andrew Brodie 2015 • www.bloomsbury.com

Overview
HOMOPHONES AND NEAR-HOMOPHONES

here	hear
knot	not
mail	male
main	mane
meat	meet
medal	meddle
missed	mist
where	wear

© Spelling for Literacy for ages 7-8 • Andrew Brodie 2015 • www.bloomsbury.com

Spelling activity sheet

NAME: _____

 Here are more words that sound the same…

 … but they are spelt differently.

Match the words on the left to the words on the right.
The first one has been done for you.

meat — meet

where   mist

not   medal

male   here

hear   wear

meddle   knot

missed   main

mane   mail

Choose the correct word to fill each gap.

Mum told me _____ we should _____ after school.

I was given a _____ when I won the race.

The dog got lost in the _____.

I couldn't _____ the radio very well.

© Spelling for Literacy for ages 7-8 • Andrew Brodie 2015 • www.bloomsbury.com

Learn, write, check

NAME: _____

Look and say	Write then cover	Write then check
here		
hear		
knot		
not		
mail		
male		
main		
mane		
meat		
meet		
medal		
meddle		
missed		
mist		
where		
wear		

peace	piece
plain	plane
rain	rein
reign	scene
seen	heel
heal	he'll
no	know
deer	dear

Spelling activity sheet

SET 33 · SHEET B

NAME: _____

Here are more words that sound the same…

… but they are spelt differently.

Match the words on the left to the words on the right.
Be careful: some words on the left will need matching to more than one word on the right!

no	dear
seen	rain
rein	know
plain	piece
heel	reign
peace	plane
deer	scene
	he'll
	heal

Choose the correct word to fill each gap.

Queen Victoria had a very long _____.

Yesterday I had a large _____ of cake.

The first _____ of the play takes place in a castle.

My _____ was very sore so I tried to _____ it with some cream.

103

Learn, write, check

NAME: _____

Look and say	Write then cover	Write then check
peace		
piece		
plain		
plane		
rain		
rein		
reign		
scene		
seen		
heel		
heal		
he'll		
no		
know		
deer		
dear		

SET 34 · SHEET A

accident	accidentally
actual	actually
address	answer
appear	believe
bicycle	breath
breathe	build
busy	business
calendar	caught

Spelling activity sheet

NAME: _____

You need to learn these words.

They are very useful!

| actual | bicycle | accidentally | busy | breathe | caught |

| actually | accident | calendar | address | appear | believe |

| breath | answer | build | business |

Which of the words begin with a?

_____ _____ _____ _____

_____ _____ _____

Which of the words begin with b?

_____ _____ _____ _____

_____ _____ _____

Which of the words begin with c?

_____ _____

Choose the correct word to fill each gap.

The boy crashed his _____ _____.

January is the first month on the _____.

It took three weeks to _____ the shed.

The teacher asked me to _____ the question.

Can you write your address?

_____

_____

_____

_____

_____

Learn, write, check

NAME: _____

Look and say	Write then cover	Write then check
accident		
accidentally		
actual		
actually		
address		
answer		
appear		
believe		
bicycle		
breath		
breathe		
build		
busy		
business		
calendar		
caught		

centre	century
certain	circle
complete	consider
continue	decide
describe	different
difficult	disappear
early	earth
eight	eighth

Spelling activity sheet

NAME: _____

Here are more useful words.

Can you learn them?

certain	difficult	continue	describe	eight	disappear
consider	decide	early	circle	different	centre
eighth	century	earth	complete		

Which of the words begin with c?

_____ _____ _____ _____

_____ _____ _____ _____

Which of the words begin with d?

_____ _____ _____ _____

_____

Which of the words begin with e?

_____ _____ _____ _____

Choose the correct word to fill each gap.

I can't _____ which word to write first.

Can you _____ your friend?

The core is at the _____ of the _____.

Write three sentences, using the words 'difficult', 'complete' and 'early'.

_____

_____

_____

_____

_____

_____

© Spelling for Literacy for ages 7-8 • Andrew Brodie 2015 • www.bloomsbury.com

Learn, write, check

SET 35 · SHEET C

NAME: _____

Look and say	Write then cover	Write then check
centre		
century		
certain		
circle		
complete		
consider		
continue		
decide		
describe		
different		
difficult		
disappear		
early		
earth		
eight		
eighth		

SET 36

SHEET A

enough	exercise
experience	experiment
extreme	famous
favourite	February
forward	forwards
fruit	grammar
group	guard
guide	heard

Spelling activity sheet

NAME: _____

Did you know there is a letter **r** in February?

Actually, there are two!

| group | experience | favourite | heard | forwards | forward |

| famous | grammar | exercise | guide | enough | experiment |

| guard | fruit | extreme | February |

Which of the words begin with e?

_____ _____ _____

_____ _____

Which of the words begin with f?

_____ _____ _____

_____ _____ _____

Which of the words begin with g?

_____ _____

_____ _____

Which of the words begin with h?

_____

Can you write the names of all the months of the year in order?

J_____	M_____	S_____
F_____	J_____	O_____
M_____	J_____	N_____
A_____	A_____	D_____

Learn, write, check

NAME: _____

Look and say	Write then cover	Write then check
enough		
exercise		
experience		
experiment		
extreme		
famous		
favourite		
February		
forward		
forwards		
fruit		
grammar		
group		
guard		
guide		
heard		

heart	height
history	imagine
increase	important
interest	island
knowledge	learn
length	library
material	medicine
mention	minute

Spelling activity sheet

NAME: _____

Here are even more words to learn!

Can you think of a word that begins with **j**?

interest | height | medicine | imagine | learn | minute

heart | island | knowledge | increase | length | material

library | history | mention | important

Which of the words begin with h?

_____ _____ _____

Which of the words begin with i?

_____ _____ _____

_____ _____

Which of the words begin with k?

_____

Which of the words begin with l?

_____ _____ _____

Which of the words begin with m?

_____ _____ _____

_____

Choose a word from each set above and write a sentence for each one.

_____

_____

_____

_____

_____

Learn, write, check

NAME: _____

Look and say	Write then cover	Write then check
heart		
height		
history		
imagine		
increase		
important		
interest		
island		
knowledge		
learn		
length		
library		
material		
medicine		
mention		
minute		

natural	naughty
notice	occasion
occasionally	often
opposite	ordinary
particular	peculiar
perhaps	popular
position	possess
possession	potatoes

Spelling activity sheet

NAME: _____

Here are more important words.

Does one of them describe you?

| position | natural | possession | occasion | often | opposite |

| ordinary | particular | naughty | peculiar | perhaps | occasionally |

| popular | possess | notice | potatoes |

Which of the words begin with n?

_____ _____ _____

Which of the words begin with o?

_____ _____ _____

_____ _____

Which of the words begin with p?

_____ _____ _____ _____

_____ _____ _____ _____

Write the correct word in each gap.

Chips and crisps are made from _____.

The _____ boy was frightening the cat.

Football is a very _____ sport.

We go to the cinema _____.

Did you _____ the new picture on the wall?

Can you write a sentence using the word 'opposite'?

_____

_____

118

Learn, write, check

NAME: _____

Look and say	Write then cover	Write then check
natural		
naughty		
notice		
occasion		
occasionally		
often		
opposite		
ordinary		
particular		
peculiar		
perhaps		
popular		
position		
possess		
possession		
potatoes		

pressure	probably
promise	purpose
quarter	question
recent	regular
reign	remember
sentence	separate
special	straight
strange	strength

Spelling activity sheet

NAME: _____

You've probably seen some of these words before.

It's good to keep practising regularly.

pressure	special	regular	strange	quarter	recent
straight	reign	probably	remember	sentence	promise
	question	strength	purpose	separate	

Which of the words begin with p?

_____   _____   _____   _____

Which of the words begin with q?

_____   _____

Which of the words begin with r?

_____   _____   _____   _____

Which of the words begin with s?

_____   _____   _____

_____   _____

Write the correct word in each gap.

A _____ always starts with a capital letter and ends

with a full stop, a question mark or an exclamation mark.

I hope you _____ that today is a _____ day:

it's my birthday!

Can you write a sentence using the word 'strength'?

_____

_____

121

© Spelling for Literacy for ages 7-8 • Andrew Brodie 2015 • www.bloomsbury.com

Learn, write, check

NAME: _____

Look and say	Write then cover	Write then check
pressure		
probably		
promise		
purpose		
quarter		
question		
recent		
regular		
reign		
remember		
sentence		
separate		
special		
straight		
strange		
strength		

Overview
WORD LIST FOR YEARS 3 AND 4

suppose	surprise
therefore	though
although	thought
through	various
weather	whether
whose	who's
weigh	weight
woman	women

Spelling activity sheet

NAME: _____

These are the last words in the book.

You always like to have the last word!

| suppose | therefore | although | whose | though | woman | whether |

| various | weather | through | surprise | weight | thought | women |

Which of the words begin with s?

_____   _____

Which of the words begin with t?

_____ _____ _____ _____

Which of the words begin with v?

_____

Which of the words begin with w?

_____ _____ _____ _____ _____

_____ _____

One word begins with a and has a partner word. Write both words.

_____   _____

Can you write a sentence using the word 'although'?

_____

Can you write a sentence using the word 'weather'?

_____

Can you write a sentence using the word 'surprise'?

_____

Learn, write, check

NAME: _____

Look and say	Write then cover	Write then check
suppose		
surprise		
therefore		
though		
although		
thought		
through		
various		
weather		
whether		
whose		
who's		
weigh		
weight		
woman		
women		

Answers

Set 1 Sheet B, p7

young younger youngest
country countries countryside
trouble troubling troublesome
touch touched touching

Set 2 Sheet B, p10

ringing
walking
jumping
painting
dressing
resting
calling

Missing words: dressing, jumping, calling, painting, ringing, singing

Set 3 Sheet B, p13

dreaming
feeling
shouting
sailing
boiling
peeling
speaking

sail > sailing
eat > eating
look > looking
sweep > sweeping
nail > nailing
treat > treating
cook > cooking

Pupil to find their own words to follow the pattern, e.g. seem > seeming
rain > raining
beat > beating
book > booking

Set 4 Sheet B, p16

hopping
sitting
skipping
stepping
gripping
shutting
winning

Missing words: skipping, skipping, gripping, shutting humming, winning, spinning, swimming, stopping

Set 5 Sheet B, p19

coming
smiling
taking
caring
making
dividing
staring
shine
tune
rhyme
time

Set 6 Sheet B, p22

pan	cake	pancake
down	stairs	downstairs
up	stairs	upstairs
any	where	anywhere
goal	keeper	goalkeeper
week	end	weekend
break	fast	breakfast
some	times	sometimes

Set 7 Sheet B, p25

twenty	thirteen
seventeen	eighty
eleven	twelve
sixty	seventy
sixteen	fourteen
nineteen	forty
fifty	eighteen
thirty	fifteen

Set 8 Sheet B, p28

1000	ninety
1000000	hundred
90	thousand
100	million

second
minute
hour

centimetre
kilometre
metre
litre
millilitre
kilogram
millimetre
gram

Answers

Set 9 Sheet B, p31

untidy
unlucky
unusual
unzip
untie
unfair
unkind

Missing words: unhappy, unzip, untie, unkind/unfair

Pupil to find appropriate words, e.g.
do > undo
steady > unsteady
pleasant > unpleasant

Set 10 Sheet B, p34

beginning
preferring
limiting

Missing words: gardener, preferred, forgotten, beginner, limited

Set 11 Sheet B, p37

misspell
disconnect
disappoint
mislead
disappear
disobey
misbehave
disloyal
misprint
disobedient
mismatch

Set 12 Sheet B, p40

crumb	halves
bomb	could
climb	palm
comb	should
thumb	half
lamb	calm
numb	calf
	calves
	would

Set 13 Sheet B, p43

knock	wrap	rhyme	gnome
knee	wrist	where	gnat
know	write	honest	gnaw

Set 14 Sheet B, p46

revisit
replay
rewrite
recycle
replace
return

Example words beginning with pre: precaution precious preconcert precondition predict prefab prefect preflight preheat premium premier

Set 15 Sheet B, p49

bicycle
recycle
tricycle
disappear
invisible
abnormal
preview
review
interview
submarine

Example words beginning with inter: international intercity interlude

Set 16 Sheet B, p52

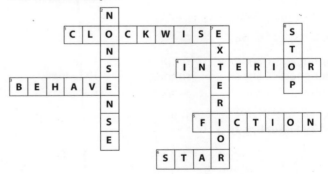

Set 17 Sheet B, p55

supermarket
superstar
immature
superman
immortal
impossible
imperfect
impatient

Answers

Set 18 Sheet B, p58

renew
reappear
submarine
redo
rewind
redecorate
subdivide
return

Set 19 Sheet B, p61

prepare	sense	inform	adore
prepared	sensation	informing	adoration
preparing	informed		
preparation	information		

Set 20 Sheet B, p64

accidental
comical
sadly
completely
actually
finally
accidentally
comically
usually

magical   magically

Set 21 Sheet B, p67

gentle	angry	simple	happy
gentleness	anger	simpler	happiness
gently	angrily	simplest	happily
	simply		

Set 22 Sheet B, p70

measure	treasure	please	enclose
measuring	treasuring	pleased	enclosed
measured	treasured	pleasing	enclosing
	pleasure	enclosure	

Set 23 Sheet B, p73

is not — couldn't
could not — didn't
have not — isn't
should not — can't
can not — won't
was not — haven't
did not — don't
will not — shouldn't
do not — doesn't
does not — wouldn't
would not — wasn't

Missing words: couldn't, wasn't, wouldn't, don't, can't

Set 24 Sheet B, p76

teacher	farmer
miner	driver
babysitter	runner
shopper	spinner

driver
farmer
teacher
babysitter
runner

Set 25 Sheet B, p79

teach	catch	furniture
rich	stretch	creature
richer	catcher	nature
teacher	stretcher	picture
	adventure	

Set 26 Sheet B, p82

poisonous
dangerous
mountainous
famous
various

poisoned poisoning tremendous enormous jealous jealousy

Set 27 Sheet B, p85

invention
hesitation
description
reflection
injection
detection
completion
action

Set 28 Sheet B, p88

expression
permission
discussion
admission
confession
possession
procession

admitting > admitted
expressing > expressed
discussing > discussed
confessing > confessed
processing > processed
possessing > possessed

Answers

Set 29 Sheet B, p91

chef	league	antique
chalet	tongue	unique
machine	dialogue	mosque
brochure	analogue	cheque
	plague	grotesque
	grotesquely	
	uniquely	

Missing words: chalet cheque chef tongue antique

Set 30 Sheet B, p94

weigh eight neigh eighteen neighbor eighth weight neighbourhood sleigh neighbourly eighty

obey they

straight

Missing words: neighbor, neigh, high, straight

Set 31 Sheet B, p97

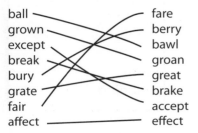

Missing words: bawl, grown, bury, fare

Set 32 Sheet B, p100

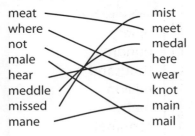

Missing words: where, meet, medal, mist, hear

Set 33 Sheet B, p103

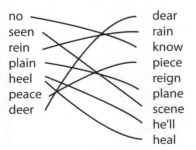

Missing words: reign, piece, scene, heel, heal

Set 34 Sheet B, p106

actual accidentally actually accident address appear answer

bicycle busy breathe believe breath build business

caught calendar

Missing words:
bicycle accidentally
calendar
build
answer

Set 35 Sheet B, p109

certain continue consider circle centre century complete difficult describe disappear decide different eight early eighth earth

Missing words: decide, describe, centre, earth

Set 36 Sheet B, p112

experience exercise enough experiment extreme favourite forwards forward famous fruit February group grammar guide guard heard

January February March April May June July August September October November December

Set 37 Sheet B, p115

heart height history
imagine increase important interest island
knowledge
learn length library
material medicine mention minute

Set 38 Sheet B, p118

natural naughty notice
occasion often opposite ordinary occasionally
position possession particular peculiar perhaps popular
possess potatoes

Missing words: potatoes, naughty, popular, occasionally, notice

Set 39 Sheet B, p121

pressure probably promise purpose
quarter question
regular recent reign remember
special strange straight sentence strength separate

Missing words: sentence, remember, special

Set 40 Sheet B, p124

suppose surprise
therefore though through thought
whose woman whether weather weight women
although though

Summary

You may wish to photocopy this page and cut it into sets, so that you can give your children a list of the words they will be focusing on each week.

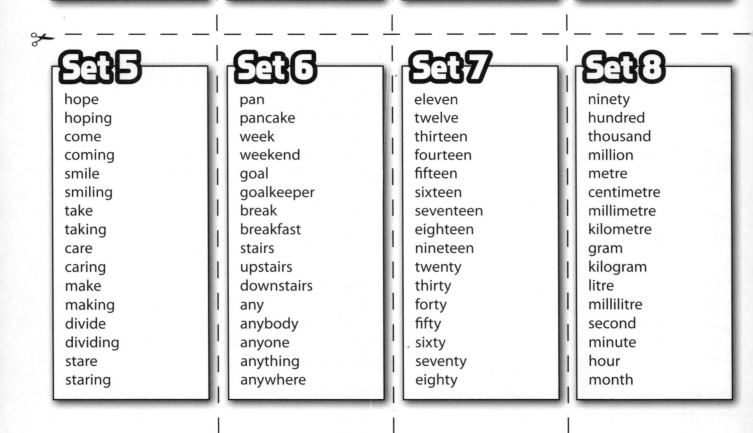

Set 1

young
younger
youngest
touch
touched
touching
double
doubling
doubled
trouble
troubling
troublesome
country
countryside
countries
couple

Set 2

sing
singing
ring
ringing
walk
walking
jump
jumping
paint
painting
dress
dressing
rest
resting
call
calling

Set 3

sleep
sleeping
dream
dreaming
feel
feeling
shout
shouting
sail
sailing
boil
boiling
peel
peeling
speak
speaking

Set 4

run
running
hop
hopping
sit
sitting
skip
skipping
step
stepping
grip
gripping
shut
shutting
win
winning

Set 5

hope
hoping
come
coming
smile
smiling
take
taking
care
caring
make
making
divide
dividing
stare
staring

Set 6

pan
pancake
week
weekend
goal
goalkeeper
break
breakfast
stairs
upstairs
downstairs
any
anybody
anyone
anything
anywhere

Set 7

eleven
twelve
thirteen
fourteen
fifteen
sixteen
seventeen
eighteen
nineteen
twenty
thirty
forty
fifty
sixty
seventy
eighty

Set 8

ninety
hundred
thousand
million
metre
centimetre
millimetre
kilometre
gram
kilogram
litre
millilitre
second
minute
hour
month

Summary

You may wish to photocopy this page and cut it into sets, so that you can give your children a list of the words they will be focusing on each week.

Set 9

happy
unhappy
tidy
untidy
lucky
unlucky
usual
unusual
zip
unzip
tie
untie
air
unfair
kind
unkind

Set 10

forget
forgetting
forgotten
begin
beginning
beginner
prefer
preferred
preferring
garden
gardening
gardened
gardener
limit
limited
limitation

Set 11

appoint
disappoint
agree
disagree
obey
disobey
connect
disconnect
appear
disappear
behave
misbehave
lead
mislead
spell
misspell

Set 12

comb
bomb
thumb
crumb
lamb
numb
climb
calf
calves
half
halves
calm
palm
could
should
would

Set 13

knee
kneel
knife
knives
know
knock
gnat
gnome
grow
write
wrist
wrap
when
where
honest
rhyme

Set 14

build
rebuild
visit
revisit
play
replay
write
rewrite
cycle
recycle
place
replace
turn
return
fresh
refresh

Set 15

cycle
bicycle
recycle
tricycle
appear
disappear
visible
invisible
normal
abnormal
view
preview
review
interview
marine
submarine

Set 16

behave
misbehave
sense
nonsense
fiction
non-fiction
stop
non-stop
import
export
interior
exterior
star
co-star
clockwise
anti-clockwise

Summary

You may wish to photocopy this page and cut it into sets, so that you can give your children a list of the words they will be focusing on each week.

Set 17

mature
immature
mortal
immortal
possible
impossible
patient
impatient
perfect
imperfect
market
supermarket
man
superman
star
superstar

Set 18

do
redo
new
renew
wind
rewind
turn
return
appear
reappear
decorate
redecorate
divide
subdivide
marine
submarine

Set 19

inform
informing
informed
information
adore
adoration
sense
sensation
prepare
preparing
prepared
preparation
admire
admired
admiring
admiration

Set 20

sad
sadly
complete
completely
actual
actually
usual
usually
final
finally
comic
comical
comically
accident
accidental
accidentally

Set 21

happy
happily
happiness
anger
angry
angrily
tidy
tidily
untidy
gentle
gently
gentleness
simple
simply
simpler
simplest

Set 22

measure
measured
measuring
treasure
treasured
treasuring
please
pleased
pleasing
pleasure
enclose
enclosing
enclosed
enclosure
leisure
leisurely

Set 23

is not
isn't
was not
wasn't
did not
didn't
does not
doesn't
will not
won't
cannot
can't
could not
couldn't
should not
shouldn't

Set 24

teach
teacher
farm
farmer
drive
driver
mine
miner
babysit
babysitter
run
runner
shop
shopper
spin
spinner

© Spelling for Literacy for ages 7-8 • Andrew Brodie 2015 • www.bloomsbury.com

Summary

You may wish to photocopy this page and cut it into sets, so that you can give your children a list of the words they will be focusing on each week.

Set 25

teach
teacher
catch
catcher
rich
richer
stretch
stretcher
creature
furniture
picture
nature
natural
naturally
adventure
adventurous

Set 26

poison
poisoning
poisoned
poisonous
danger
dangerous
mountain
mountainous
fame
famous
vary
various
tremendous
enormous
jealous
jealousy

Set 27

invent
invention
inject
injection
act
action
hesitate
hesitation
complete
completion
describe
description
detect
detection
reflect
reflection

Set 28

express
expression
discuss
discussing
discussed
discussion
confess
confession
permit
permission
admit
admission
possess
possession
process
procession

Set 29

chef
chalet
machine
brochure
league
tongue
dialogue
analogue
plague
antique
unique
mosque
cheque
grotesque
grotesquely
uniquely

Set 30

vein
weigh
weight
eight
eighth
eighty
eighteen
neigh
neighbour
neighbourly
neighbourhood
high
they
obey
straight
sleigh

Set 31

accept
except
affect
effect
ball
bawl
berry
bury
brake
break
fair
fare
grate
great
groan
grown

Set 32

here
hear
knot
not
mail
male
main
mane
meat
meet
medal
meddle
missed
mist
where
wear

133

Summary

You may wish to photocopy this page and cut it into sets, so that you can give your children a list of the words they will be focusing on each week.

Set 33

peace
piece
plain
plane
rain
rein
reign
scene
seen
heel
heal
he'll
no
know
deer
dear

Set 34

accident
accidentally
actual
actually
address
answer
appear
believe
bicycle
breath
breathe
build
busy
business
calendar
caught

Set 35

centre
century
certain
circle
complete
consider
continue
decide
describe
different
difficult
disappear
early
earth
eight
eighth

Set 36

enough
exercise
experience
experiment
extreme
famous
favourite
February
forward
forwards
fruit
grammar
group
guard
guide
heard

Set 37

heart
height
history
imagine
increase
important
interest
island
knowledge
learn
length
library
material
medicine
mention
minute

Set 38

natural
naughty
notice
occasion
occasionally
often
opposite
ordinary
particular
peculiar
perhaps
popular
position
possess
possession
potatoes

Set 39

pressure
probably
promise
purpose
quarter
question
recent
regular
reign
remember
sentence
separate
special
straight
strange
strength

Set 40

suppose
surprise
therefore
though
although
thought
through
various
weather
whether
whose
who's
weigh
weight
woman
women